Lexee Booshay is a self-inspired writer who turns her gloom into power through her writing and is fascinated with the gift to live an earthly life. She's a self-publisher going mainstream with her first book, *Momma, What Is God?* Her daughter, the ultimate power in her life's gloom, is the inspiration for devising real-life conversations for parents to facilitate the wonderous and challenging topics such as God. Her passion in life is adding value and she channels it through her writing to inspire other humans to achieve the best possible versions of themselves.

Momma, what is God?

Lexee Booshay

AUSTIN MACAULEY PUBLISHERS™
LONDON · CAMBRIDGE · NEW YORK · SHARJAH

A CIP catalogue record for this title is available from the British Library.

ISBN 9781528946247 (Paperback)
ISBN 9781528946469 (Hardback)
ISBN 9781528971683 (ePub e-book)

www.austinmacauley.com

First Published (2021)
Austin Macauley Publishers Ltd
25 Canada Square
Canary Wharf
London
E14 5LQ

Because of you, My Daughter.

"Momma, what is God?"

"God is a feeling."

"A feeling about what?"

"A feeling about a belief in how the world was created, how we should live, and where we go when we die."

"I've never thought about these things. What are the answers?"

"My Daughter, come and let's take a walk.

"Do you see all these beautiful buildings?"

"Yeah, what are they?"
"These are places where people gather to worship their belief about their feelings of God."

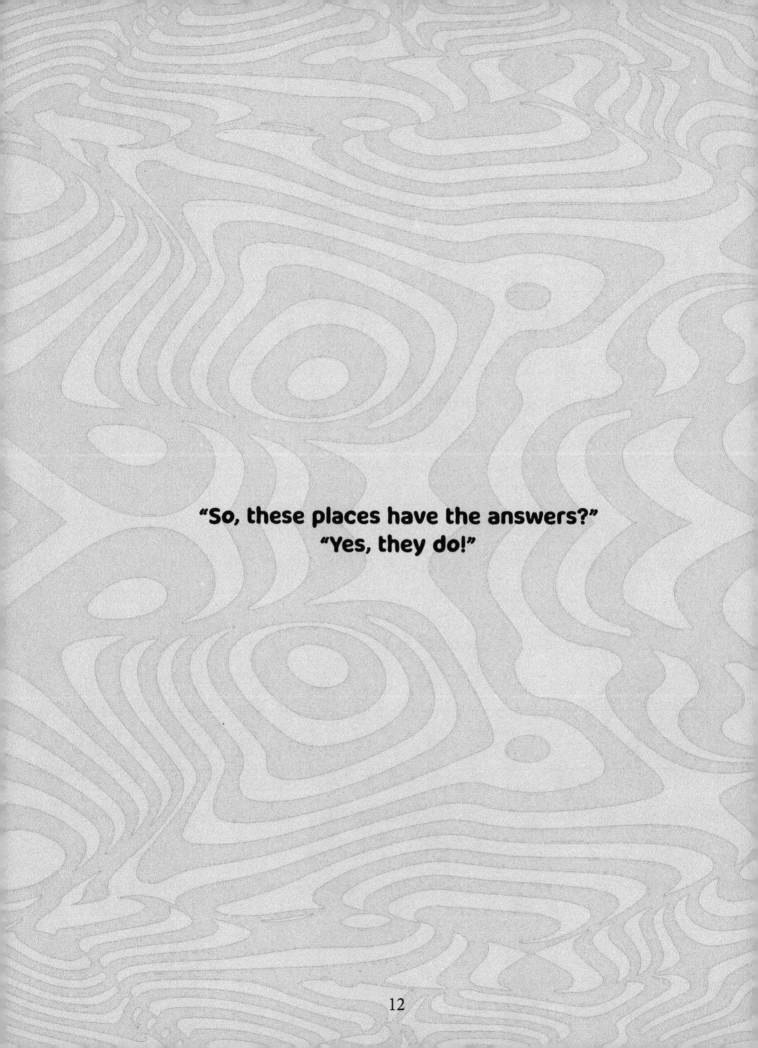

"So, these places have the answers?"
"Yes, they do!"

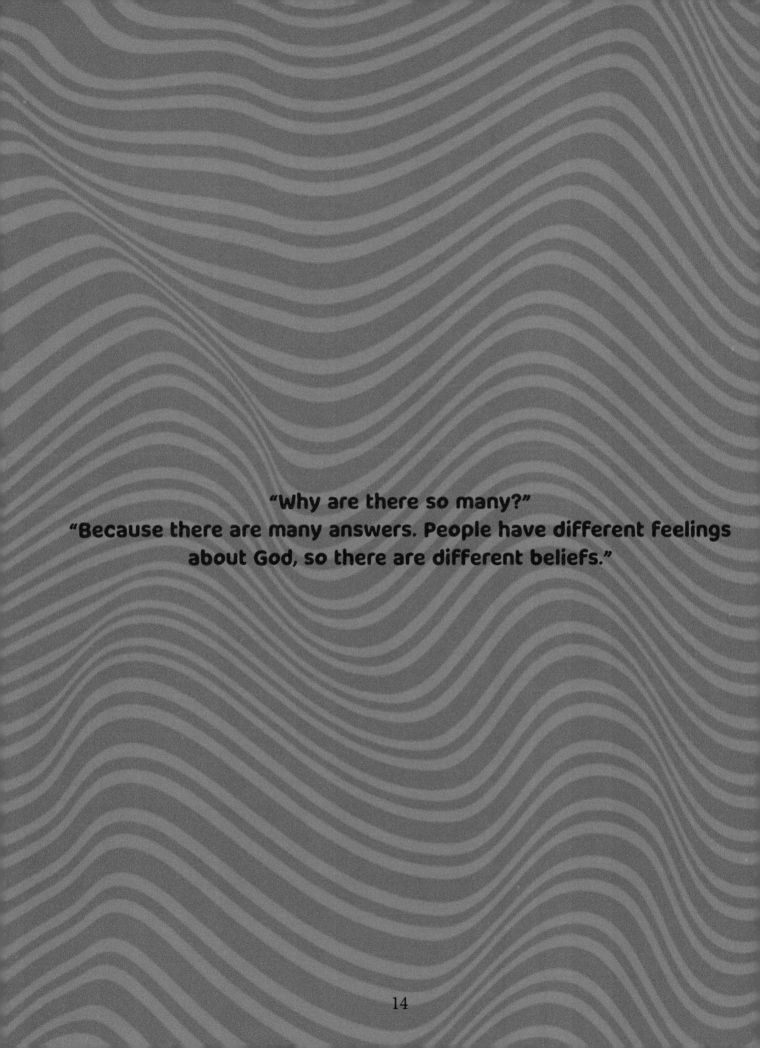

"Why are there so many?"
"Because there are many answers. People have different feelings about God, so there are different beliefs."

"But which one is right?"
"This is not for me to tell you, My Daughter."
"But shouldn't I go to the same building as you? Shouldn't I believe
what you believe?"

"You must believe in the things that feel right for YOU – not me or anyone else. And not everyone has to go to a building."
"Do you go to a building?"
"I've been to some of these buildings before, but currently I don't go to any."

"Does this mean you don't believe in anything?"
"Oh no, My Daughter. It doesn't mean that at all."

"What do you believe, Momma?"
"I believe in everything! I believe there's a power
bigger than us and it brought us to Earth,
to Love one another."
"I want to believe in something too!"

"Believing in things that make us better is a magical experience!"

"Will you help me, Momma?"
"Of course, My Daughter."
"Would you like for me to visit a building with you?"
"Oh yes! I'd like that."
"What if I don't like it though?"
"Then we'll visit another one. We'll visit them all if you'd like."

"Thank you, Momma, and I Love you!"
"I Love you too, Lotus Ann, and the light in me will always honour the light in you!"

CPSIA information can be obtained
at www.ICGtesting.com
Printed in the USA
LVHW072013220921
698451LV00018B/536